TEST YOUR TIMING

Everyone likes to hold a good hand, but good cards bring their own problems. You may hold all the right cards and come to grief by playing them in the wrong order. Accurate timing is the key to success, whether you are playing in a simple part-score contract or a complicated slam.

If you sometimes have trouble with the timing of your plays, this book will help to set matters right. Author Hugh Kelsey, a grand master of bridge and a writer of world renown, invites you to test your skill in a quiz that starts at elementary level and advances gradually to more complex situations.

After absorbing the painless lessons of this book, you will find a miraculous difference in your timing. As your hits increase and your misses diminish, you will experience the heightened pleasure and prestige that come from improved results.

Also by Hugh Kelsey

TEST YOUR TRUMP CONTROL
TEST YOUR FINESSING
TEST YOUR CARD-READING
TEST YOUR COMMUNICATIONS
TEST YOUR PERCENTAGES
INSTANT GUIDE TO BRIDGE
START BRIDGE THE EASY WAY
SLAM BIDDING
WINNING CARD PLAY
ADVENTURES IN CARD PLAY (WITH GEZA OTTLIK)
BRIDGE ODDS FOR PRACTICAL PLAYERS
(WITH MICHAEL GLAUERT)
IMPROVE YOUR OPENING LEADS (WITH JOHN MATHESON)

TEST YOUR TIMING

by

HUGH KELSEY

LONDON
VICTOR GOLLANCZ LTD
in association with Peter Crawley
1983

© Hugh Kelsey 1983

British Library Cataloguing in Publication Data
Kelsey, H. W.
    Test your timing. – (Master bridge series)
    1. Contract bridge
    I. Title
    795.41'53   GV1282.3

    ISBN 0-575-03309-6

Printed in Great Britain at
The Camelot Press Ltd, Southampton

TEST YOUR TIMING

INTRODUCTION

Accurate timing is a vital factor in every field of human endeavour. In business, sport or politics, a well-timed coup will always have a reasonable chance of success. When the timing is at fault, failure is the most likely result.

It is exactly the same at the bridge table. On most hands the outcome is determined not only by the cards that are held but also by the order in which they are played. A collection of cards that produces seven or eight tricks in the hands of a beginner may be worth ten or eleven tricks when an expert is at the wheel. The difference is in the timing.

The concept extends over the whole range of card-play technique. The time factor may play an important role in a simple suit establishment. Precise timing is vital for communication plays, cross-ruff hands, and all cases where the trumps have a lot of work to do. Endings such as squeezes, trump coups and throw-ins are even more dependent on the time factor. Players usually go astray through lack of foresight in the planning stage. It is all too easy to embark on an optimistic line of play that depends on favourable breaks and kindly opponents. When the unexpected happens it is probably too late to do anything about it. The timing is hopelessly wrong and defeat is inevitable. The only remedy is to carry out a comprehensive survey before playing to the first trick. Once you recognise the potential hazards, you have a better chance of timing the play so as to overcome them.

This quiz is designed to test your sense of timing in a wide variety of situations. The problems are set on odd-numbered pages in order to reduce the temptation to look at the answers. As usual, the bidding sequences can be ignored except where they provide clues to the enemy holdings. The opening lead is stated and in some cases the play to the first few tricks is given before the problem is posed. Try to work out the answer for yourself before reading on.

At the foot of the page the hazards are noted and the options reviewed. The solution and the complete deal can be found overleaf. No attempt has been made to arrange the material in thematic order, but the problems do tend to become progressively more difficult.

You have reason to be satisfied with your sense of timing if you come up with the right answer to twenty or more of these problems. Twenty-five right is an excellent score, and thirty right puts you in the expert class. Good luck!

PROBLEM 1

♠ A 8 7 3
♡ Q 10 8 7 2
♢ 6
♣ 8 6 3

```
    N
  W   E
    S
```

♠ K Q 10 9 2
♡ J 6 4
♢ K Q J 8 4
♣ –

Game all
Dealer East

The Bidding

WEST	NORTH	EAST	SOUTH
		1 ♣	1 ♠
3 ♣	3 ♠	Pass	4 ♠
Pass	Pass	Pass	

The Lead

West leads the king of clubs. You ruff and cash the king of spades, West following with the five and East with the four. How should you continue?

Review

Although there are only three losers in sight – two hearts and a diamond – your control is somewhat precarious. Perhaps it is as well that a heart was not led, for it looks as though the defenders could have negotiated a heart ruff. Clearly you must draw trumps before attempting to establish winners in the red suits. Are there any hidden snags?

Solution

If trumps are 2–2 there will be no difficulty. Your problem is to find the best way of countering a 3–1 break. Suppose you play a spade to the ace and someone shows out. You will have to draw a third round of trumps, and when you tackle the hearts a defender will win and return a club, taking out your last trump. When you concede the next heart the defenders will be in a position to cash a club trick, putting you one down.

This embarrassment can be avoided if you plan to win the third round of trumps in dummy. Cash the queen of spades at trick three and continue, if necessary, with a third trump to the ace. On the bidding East is likely to have the ace of diamonds, and when you play a diamond from dummy after drawing trumps he will be caught in a dilemma. If he takes his ace, you will have enough tricks for game with six trumps and four diamonds. If he plays low, allowing you to win a diamond, you can switch to hearts. Now you can expect to score six trumps, three hearts and a diamond.

The complete deal:

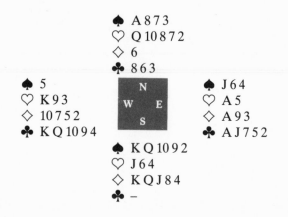

```
              ♠ A 8 7 3
              ♡ Q 10 8 7 2
              ◇ 6
              ♣ 8 6 3
♠ 5                            ♠ J 6 4
♡ K 9 3          N             ♡ A 5
◇ 10 7 5 2    W     E          ◇ A 9 3
♣ K Q 10 9 4      S            ♣ A J 7 5 2
              ♠ K Q 10 9 2
              ♡ J 6 4
              ◇ K Q J 8 4
              ♣ —
```

PROBLEM 2

♠ J 9 7 5 4 2
♡ 8 7 3
♢ 3
♣ K 8 5

♠ A
♡ K Q J 9 6
Game all   ♢ A K Q 6 5
Dealer South   ♣ 10 3

The Bidding

SOUTH	WEST	NORTH	EAST
2 ♡	Pass	2 NT	Pass
3 ♢	Pass	3 ♡	Pass
4 ♡	Pass	Pass	Pass

The Lead

West leads the seven of clubs and the jack wins the trick when you play low from dummy. East cashes the ace of clubs on which his partner plays the nine, and continues with the six of clubs. You discard a diamond, West plays the club four and dummy's king wins. How do you plan the play?

Review

It looks a simple hand. You have to bank on a normal 3–2 trump break, and you should lose just one further trick to the ace of hearts. Your diamond loser can be ruffed in dummy. Are there any snags?

[11]

Solution

Carelessness could easily lead to the loss of a second trump trick. From the play to the first few tricks it looks as though East may have started with a five-card club suit. If he also has the ace of hearts you cannot afford to relax. Suppose you play a diamond to the ace, ruff a diamond, and play a trump to your king, which wins. Now you will have to guess whether to continue with a high heart, playing for East to have three trumps, or a small one, playing him for ace doubleton. If you make the wrong decision the defenders will have their second trump trick.

All this guesswork is avoided by better timing. At trick four you should play a trump from the table. If the king wins, you can cash the diamond ace, ruff the small diamond in dummy and play another trump. Whether East began with two or three trumps, he has to waste his ace on air and there is no risk of a trump promotion.

The complete deal:

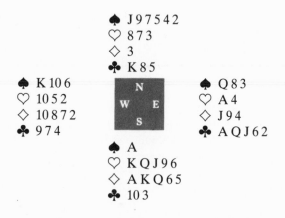

```
              ♠ J97542
              ♡ 873
              ◇ 3
              ♣ K85
  ♠ K106      ┌─────────┐    ♠ Q83
  ♡ 1052      │    N    │    ♡ A4
  ◇ 10872     │ W     E │    ◇ J94
  ♣ 974       │    S    │    ♣ AQJ62
              └─────────┘
              ♠ A
              ♡ KQJ96
              ◇ AKQ65
              ♣ 103
```

PROBLEM 3

♠ 4
♡ A 10 7
♢ A Q J 7 6
♣ Q 8 6 3

```
    N
 W     E
    S
```

♠ A 8 3
♡ Q J
♢ K 10 8
♣ K 7 5 4 2

Game all
Dealer South

The Bidding

SOUTH	WEST	NORTH	EAST
1 ♣	Pass	1 ♢	2 ♠
Pass	Pass	4 ♣	Pass
5 ♣	Pass	Pass	Pass

The Lead

West leads the ten of spades to the jack and ace. How do you plan the play?

Review

On the bidding the ace of clubs is likely to be in the East hand. So there must be a case for entering dummy at trick two – either with a diamond or with a spade ruff – and playing a low club from the table. This gives you the best chance of avoiding two club losers. Is there any reason to reject this line of play?

[13]

Solution

Although East is the favourite to hold the ace of clubs, there can be no certainty in the matter. And it would be highly dangerous to play a low club to the king if West had the ace. In that case the king of hearts would surely be with East, and a heart switch from West would threaten you with the loss of two clubs and a heart.

On this hand you can afford to lose two trump tricks as long as you do not lose a heart. Correct timing is achieved by the simple play of a club to the queen at trick two. East may win, but he can do no harm from his side of the table. After regaining the lead you can draw a second round of trumps, and you will be able to dispose of the heart loser and one spade loser on the long diamonds.

If the queen of clubs wins at trick two, you simply abandon trumps and play on diamonds. West is welcome to ruff the third diamond and return a heart, for you can go up with the ace and throw your heart loser on the fourth diamond.

The complete deal:

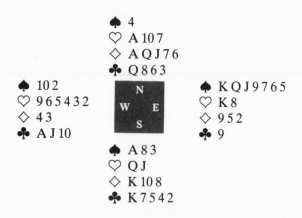

```
                    ♠ 4
                    ♡ A 10 7
                    ◇ A Q J 7 6
                    ♣ Q 8 6 3
   ♠ 10 2              N           ♠ K Q J 9 7 6 5
   ♡ 9 6 5 4 3 2    W     E        ♡ K 8
   ◇ 4 3              S            ◇ 9 5 2
   ♣ A J 10                        ♣ 9
                    ♠ A 8 3
                    ♡ Q J
                    ◇ K 10 8
                    ♣ K 7 5 4 2
```

PROBLEM 4

♠ 6
♡ A 8 3
◇ A 9 6 4
♣ A K 10 6 2

♠ J 8 3
♡ K Q 7 6 5
◇ 7 5
♣ Q J 4

E–W game
Dealer North

The Bidding

WEST	NORTH	EAST	SOUTH
	1 ♣	Pass	1 ♡
Pass	2 ◇	Pass	2 ♡
Pass	4 ♡	Pass	Pass
Pass			

The Lead

West leads the ace of spades and switches to the queen of diamonds. How do you plan the play?

Review

It looks as though you may have to underbid this one, for twelve tricks could be within reach. If you win the ace of diamonds, play a club to the queen, ruff a spade and draw trumps, you can hope to score six trump tricks, one diamond and five clubs. Are there any dangers in this line of play?

Solution

Playing for the maximum is fraught with danger and would be correct only in a pairs tournament. At no other form of the game can you afford to assume that trumps will break evenly. If someone showed out of the second round of trumps you would be left with four losers – two spades, a trump and a diamond.

If a trump trick has to be lost, you must arrange to lose it while dummy still has a trump to control the spades. Moreover, you cannot afford to win the first diamond, for you might then lose *two* trump tricks. Duck the queen of diamonds, win the continuation, cash the ace of hearts, and concede the second round of trumps to the defenders. Now you can cope with any return and can be reasonably sure of ten tricks.

The complete deal:

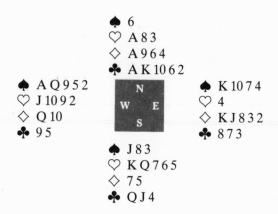

PROBLEM 5

```
          ♠ 7 6 5
          ♡ 8 6 4 3
          ◇ K 10 7
          ♣ Q 5 2
```

```
              N
           W     E
              S
```

```
          ♠ A K Q 4 2
          ♡ A
Game all   ◇ A Q 3
Dealer South  ♣ A K 6 3
```

The Bidding

SOUTH	WEST	NORTH	EAST
2 ♣	Pass	2 ◇	Pass
2 ♠	Pass	2 NT	Pass
3 ♣	Pass	3 ♠	Pass
4 ◇	Pass	5 ♣	Pass
6 ♠	Pass	Pass	Pass

The Lead

West leads the queen of hearts to your ace. Both opponents follow when you cash the ace of spades, but West discards the four of hearts on the second round. How should you continue?

Review

The hand looked simple to begin with, but the 4–1 trump break has complicated matters. There is no way of avoiding a trump loser, so you must take care not to lose a club trick as well. You will naturally have no worries on a 3–3 club break. Can you cope if the clubs are 4–2 or worse?

Solution

The contract is cold provided that East has at least one club. You have to time the play so as to give East no chance of ruffing one of your club winners. There is no objection to his ruffing a loser, for the rest of the tricks will then be yours.

Play a small club to the queen at trick four and return the suit. If East is able and willing to ruff, he will be ruffing your loser. If East follows suit or discards, win with the king, return to dummy with the king of diamonds, and continue with a third club. If unable to follow, East will be faced with the same choice of ruffing a loser or allowing your ace to score. If he chooses the latter course, you can ruff the fourth club with dummy's last trump, restricting East to one trick whether he takes it now or later. If East proves to have four or more clubs, of course, you will be able to enjoy your club ruff in peace.

The complete deal:

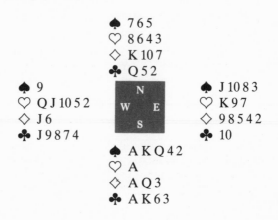

```
                    ♠ 7 6 5
                    ♡ 8 6 4 3
                    ♢ K 10 7
                    ♣ Q 5 2
     ♠ 9                              ♠ J 10 8 3
     ♡ Q J 10 5 2                     ♡ K 9 7
     ♢ J 6                            ♢ 9 8 5 4 2
     ♣ J 9 8 7 4                      ♣ 10
                    ♠ A K Q 4 2
                    ♡ A
                    ♢ A Q 3
                    ♣ A K 6 3
```

PROBLEM 6

```
              ♠ A 5
              ♡ K 7 6 4
              ♢ A J 10 6 2
              ♣ 8 3
```

```
                 N
              W     E
                 S
```

```
              ♠ J 8
              ♡ A 10 5 3 2
Love all      ♢ K 5 3
Dealer North  ♣ A 7 6
```

The Bidding

WEST	NORTH	EAST	SOUTH
	1 ♢	Pass	1 ♡
Pass	2 ♡	Pass	4 ♡
Pass	Pass	Pass	

The Lead

West leads the queen of clubs. It is clearly not an occasion for holding up, so you win with the ace, play a low heart to the king and return a heart to your ace. Unkindly, East discards a spade on the second round. How should you continue?

Review

The position does not look too bad. There is a sure loser in trumps and another in clubs, but you can afford to lose a diamond trick as long as you do not lose a spade as well. What is the right way to organise the play?

Solution

You could finesse either way against the queen of diamonds, but this would be unsound. After a losing diamond finesse and a spade return, you might go down in a cold contract. With fewer than three diamonds West would be able to ruff with his master trump and cash a spade trick before you could negotiate your discard.

The contract is completely safe unless West is void in diamonds. Cash the king of diamonds at trick four and continue with a diamond to the ace. If the queen does not fall, persevere with the jack of diamonds, conceding a trick to the defenders. Now a spade switch can do no harm, for after winning the ace you can discard your spade loser on the established ten of diamonds.

The complete deal:

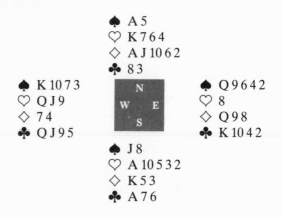

```
              ♠ A 5
              ♡ K 7 6 4
              ◇ A J 10 6 2
              ♣ 8 3
  ♠ K 10 7 3                  ♠ Q 9 6 4 2
  ♡ Q J 9         N           ♡ 8
  ◇ 7 4       W       E       ◇ Q 9 8
  ♣ Q J 9 5       S           ♣ K 10 4 2
              ♠ J 8
              ♡ A 10 5 3 2
              ◇ K 5 3
              ♣ A 7 6
```

If West had started with a singleton diamond, East might play low on the third round, allowing his partner to ruff. But after winning the spade return you would be able to ruff out the queen of diamonds and return to dummy with a trump to take your discard.

PROBLEM 7

♠ A 8 6 2
♡ K 5 3
♢ Q J 10 8 3
♣ 4

```
        N
    W       E
        S
```

N–S game
Dealer East

♠ Q 5
♡ A Q 10 8 6 2
♢ 6 4
♣ A 9 3

The Bidding

WEST	NORTH	EAST	SOUTH
		Pass	1 ♡
Pass	2 ♢	Pass	2 ♡
Pass	3 ♡	Pass	4 ♡
Pass	Pass	Pass	

The Lead

West leads the nine of diamonds to the queen and king, and East switches to the ten of spades. How do you plan the play?

Review

On the face of it there are no more than three losers, but the going may become rough if the trumps are 3–1 and West has the king of spades. With the ace of spades inconveniently removed from dummy, you will have to rely on the king of hearts as an entry for the established diamonds, and there is some danger of an enemy trump promotion.

East would no doubt switch to a spade at trick two whether he held the king or not. What is the best chance?

Solution

There is good reason to suspect that the king of spades is with West. East is marked with the top diamonds and also, since West failed to lead a club, with one of the club honours. Holding the king of spades as well he would surely have opened the bidding.

For reasons of control it is important to play the five of spades at trick two, retaining the queen. Win with the ace and test the trumps with the ace and queen. If East shows out on the second round you can continue with a diamond to the jack and ace. Now East will be in a quandary. He can give his partner a diamond ruff, it is true, but only at the cost of the defensive spade trick. If instead East plays a spade to his partner's king, the defenders will have no way of obtaining their diamond ruff.

The complete hand:

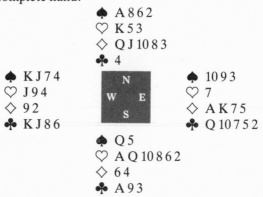

```
                    ♠ A 8 6 2
                    ♡ K 5 3
                    ◇ Q J 10 8 3
                    ♣ 4
 ♠ K J 7 4                            ♠ 10 9 3
 ♡ J 9 4           N                  ♡ 7
 ◇ 9 2          W     E               ◇ A K 7 5
 ♣ K J 8 6         S                  ♣ Q 10 7 5 2
                    ♠ Q 5
                    ♡ A Q 10 8 6 2
                    ◇ 6 4
                    ♣ A 9 3
```

Covering the ten of spades at trick two results in defeat. On winning the second diamond East cashes the nine of spades, holding the trick, and then plays a diamond to promote a trump trick for his partner.

PROBLEM 8

♠ J
♡ K 6 3
♢ K J 10 9 8 3
♣ 6 4 2

```
        N
    W       E
        S
```

♠ K Q 6 5 2
♡ A Q J
♢ Q
♣ K J 10 5

Game all
Dealer South

The Bidding

SOUTH	WEST	NORTH	EAST
1 ♠	Pass	2 ♢	Pass
3 NT	Pass	Pass	Pass

The Lead

West leads the ten of hearts to your jack. How do you plan the play?

Review

There are three quick winners and it should be possible to establish five tricks in diamonds and two more in spades for a total of ten tricks.

Cross-check by counting losers. There is one loser in spades, one in diamonds and at most two in clubs. Is there any danger that you might lose a fifth trick?

Solution

It is easy to overlook the difficulties that may ensue if you play a diamond at trick two. Someone will win and return a heart, and you will have to win in dummy in order to preserve a later entry to your hand. On the run of the diamonds you will be able to throw the small club and three spades without pain, but the play of the last diamond will force you to weaken your hand in some way. No doubt you will throw another club, but you will now be in danger of defeat when East has the ace of spades and West has both club honours.

Better timing solves the problem. The right move is to play a spade to the jack at trick two. If this loses to the ace and a heart comes back, win in hand with the ace, cash one high spade for a club discard, and then play on diamonds, overtaking the queen with the king to force out the ace and establish your nine tricks.

The complete deal:

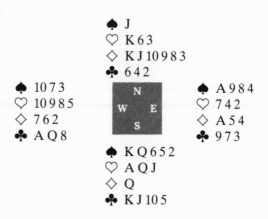

```
                    ♠ J
                    ♡ K 6 3
                    ◇ K J 10 9 8 3
                    ♣ 6 4 2
    ♠ 10 7 3              N              ♠ A 9 8 4
    ♡ 10 9 8 5        W       E          ♡ 7 4 2
    ◇ 7 6 2              S              ◇ A 5 4
    ♣ A Q 8                              ♣ 9 7 3
                    ♠ K Q 6 5 2
                    ♡ A Q J
                    ◇ Q
                    ♣ K J 10 5
```

If you play on diamonds at trick two, careful discarding by the defenders will always defeat the contract.

PROBLEM 9

♠ J 7 3
♥ A Q 7 5 4
♦ 5 2
♣ A 7 4

```
        N
    W       E
        S
```

♠ A K 8 6 4
♥ 9 3
♦ A 8 7
♣ Q 8 2

Love all
Dealer South

The Bidding

SOUTH	WEST	NORTH	EAST
1 ♠	2 ♦	2 ♥	Pass
2 ♠	Pass	3 ♠	Pass
4 ♠	Pass	Pass	Pass

The Lead

West leads the king of diamonds and continues with the queen. East follows with the three and the six, and you take your ace on the second round. How should you continue?

Review

It will not help to find someone with a doubleton queen of spades since you need to ruff a diamond in dummy. You must budget for losing a spade as well as a diamond, and the problem is to avoid the loss of more than one trick in the other suits. On the bidding the heart finesse is likely to work, but there is no guarantee that East will have the king of clubs. What chances have you when the king of clubs is badly placed?

Solution

A successful heart finesse will make a certainty of your contract when the trumps are 3–2 and the hearts no worse than 4–2. But you have to be careful over the timing. It would be a mistake to take your diamond ruff immediately, for this would remove a vital entry from dummy. The right approach is to tackle the hearts first. Cash the ace and king of spades and then play a heart for a finesse of the queen. When it wins, continue with the heart ace and a heart ruff. If the hearts are 3–3 you will actually make an overtrick. Ruff the diamond and play a fourth heart, discarding a club from hand. A defender may ruff with the master trump and attack clubs, but you win with the ace and discard your remaining club loser on the last heart.

There will be no overtrick in the more likely event that the hearts are 4–2, but your contract will still be secure. After ruffing the third heart you return to dummy with a diamond ruff and establish the hearts with a further ruff. Now a club to the ace puts dummy in, and one of your losing clubs goes away as a defender ruffs with the master trump.

The complete deal:

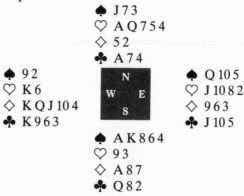

```
                    ♠ J 7 3
                    ♡ A Q 7 5 4
                    ◇ 5 2
                    ♣ A 7 4
      ♠ 9 2              N              ♠ Q 10 5
      ♡ K 6          W       E          ♡ J 10 8 2
      ◇ K Q J 10 4       S              ◇ 9 6 3
      ♣ K 9 6 3                         ♣ J 10 5
                    ♠ A K 8 6 4
                    ♡ 9 3
                    ◇ A 8 7
                    ♣ Q 8 2
```

PROBLEM 10

♠ Q 8 4
♡ 8 7 3
♢ A 5 2
♣ A Q J 10

♠ K 6 5 2
♡ A K
♢ K Q 9
♣ 9 8 6 4

Love all
Dealer South

The Bidding

SOUTH	WEST	NORTH	EAST
1 NT	Pass	3 NT	Pass
Pass	Pass		

The Lead

West leads the queen of hearts to the three, four and king. How do you plan the play?

Review

You can count six winners and three extra tricks may be made in clubs if the finesse is right. Failing that, there is always the possibility of scoring a trick in spades. The trouble is that you can afford to lose the lead only once before the enemy hearts are established. What is the best sequence of play?

Solution

If you take a losing club finesse a heart will come back, and you will be sunk unless West started with six hearts and no entry. There is, of course, no hurry to try the club finesse. The best shot is to tackle spades first, hoping to slip past the ace. If you play it the right way the manoeuvre is bound to succeed when the spades are 3–3, for a defender cannot go up with the ace without allowing you to score three spade tricks. Who is most likely to have the ace of spades?

Although there is no clue to the location of the ace of spades, the right move is to cross to dummy with the ace of diamonds and play a low spade to your king. If it wins you can make sure of nine tricks by switching to clubs.

The complete deal:

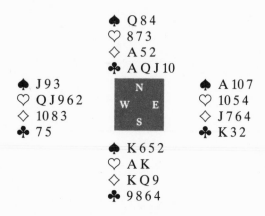

```
              ♠ Q 8 4
              ♡ 8 7 3
              ◇ A 5 2
              ♣ A Q J 10
 ♠ J 9 3                      ♠ A 10 7
 ♡ Q J 9 6 2      N           ♡ 10 5 4
 ◇ 10 8 3      W     E        ◇ J 7 6 4
 ♣ 7 5           S            ♣ K 3 2
              ♠ K 6 5 2
              ♡ A K
              ◇ K Q 9
              ♣ 9 8 6 4
```

It is true that it could have been right to play the spades the other way round, but this play is more hazardous. East might hold ♠ A J 10 x x, a doubleton heart and the king of clubs, in which case his spade continuation would defeat a contract that could have been made.

PROBLEM 11

♠ 3
♡ K 7 4
◇ A K 9 6 5 4
♣ K 10 3

♠ A 6 2
♡ A 8 6 5 3
◇ 2
♣ A J 7 5

Game all
Dealer North

The Bidding

WEST	NORTH	EAST	SOUTH
	1 ◇	Pass	1 ♡
Pass	2 ♡	Pass	2 ♠
Pass	3 ◇	Pass	4 ♣
Pass	5 ♡	Pass	6 ♡
Pass	Pass	Pass	

The Lead

West leads the jack of spades to the three, eight and ace. How do you plan the play?

Review

Naturally you must hope for a 3–2 trump break. You could try to set up the diamond suit, or you could ruff two spades in dummy and rely on taking a winning view in clubs. Which is the correct line of play?

Solution

Given an even trump break, the contract is always safe if the diamonds are no worse than 4–2. There is no need to hazard a club finesse, and only one spade need be ruffed in dummy. Your twelve tricks should consist of the ace of spades and a spade ruff, four trumps in your own hand, four diamonds and two clubs. The timing has to be precise, however.

After winning the ace of spades you should play a diamond to the ace and ruff a diamond. The ace of hearts is followed by a heart to the king, a spade is discarded on the king of diamonds, and a further diamond is ruffed if necessary. Now a spade ruff gives access to dummy, and the club losers are discarded on the established diamonds. A defender may ruff at any time with the master trump, but that is the only trick for the defence.

The complete deal:

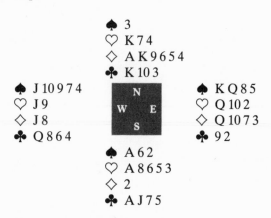

♠ 3
♡ K 7 4
♢ A K 9 6 5 4
♣ K 10 3

♠ J 10 9 7 4
♡ J 9
♢ J 8
♣ Q 8 6 4

♠ K Q 8 5
♡ Q 10 2
♢ Q 10 7 3
♣ 9 2

♠ A 6 2
♡ A 8 6 5 3
♢ 2
♣ A J 7 5

If you attempt to ruff two spades in dummy, or if you cash the top hearts before ruffing a diamond, you will be forced to fall back upon the club finesse.

PROBLEM 12

♠ A 6 5
♡ 7 4 3
♢ Q 7 2
♣ A K 9 2

♠ K 8 7 4 3
♡ A K 8 5
♢ K 5
♣ 7 6

Game all
Dealer North

The Bidding

WEST	NORTH	EAST	SOUTH
	1 NT	Pass	2 ♣
Pass	2 ♢	Pass	3 ♠
Pass	4 ♠	Pass	Pass
Pass			

The Lead

West leads the ten of diamonds. You play low from dummy, East contributes the six and you win with the king. How should you plan the play?

Review

Again you have to rely on a 3–2 trump break. Your sure losers are a spade, a heart and a diamond, and there is some danger of losing a second heart trick. How do you overcome this threat?

Solution

There will be no difficulty if the hearts break evenly. If hearts are 4–2, you must plan to ruff the fourth heart in dummy, but there are problems in the timing. Suppose you play off the top trumps and continue with three rounds of hearts. The defender who wins the third heart may be in a position to extract dummy's last trump and then cash another heart, saddling you with four losers. It is no better to play three rounds of hearts before touching trumps. Now the danger is that a fourth round of hearts may promote a second trump trick for the defence.

In order to make the contract whenever it can be made you must play a low heart from hand at trick two. This retains control of the situation. On regaining the lead you can cash the ace and king of trumps and then play the hearts from the top. If someone ruffs with the master trump, the remaining trump in dummy will take care of your heart loser.

The complete deal:

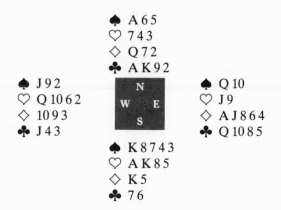

```
                    ♠ A 6 5
                    ♡ 7 4 3
                    ◇ Q 7 2
                    ♣ A K 9 2
    ♠ J 9 2                         ♠ Q 10
    ♡ Q 10 6 2          N           ♡ J 9
    ◇ 10 9 3        W       E       ◇ A J 8 6 4
    ♣ J 4 3            S            ♣ Q 10 8 5
                    ♠ K 8 7 4 3
                    ♡ A K 8 5
                    ◇ K 5
                    ♣ 7 6
```

PROBLEM 13

♠ A 9 4
♡ K 6
♢ Q 10
♣ A K Q J 8 5

♠ Q 8 7
♡ A Q 10 9 8 3
♢ J 5 3
♣ 2

Game all
Dealer North

The Bidding

WEST	NORTH	EAST	SOUTH
	2 NT	Pass	4 ♡
Pass	6 ♡	Pass	Pass
Pass			

The Lead

West leads the seven of clubs to the ace, three and two. How should you proceed?

Review

Partner's bidding has all the hallmarks of a player who is desperate for a swing. In the absence of a diamond lead, the gamble looks like paying off. If both hearts and clubs behave reasonably you will be able to take all thirteen tricks. What is the correct sequence of play?

[33]

Solution

You have to bear in mind that you need twelve tricks, not thirteen. There is nothing that can be done about a bad trump break, but it would be a pity to be brought down by a 5–1 club break.

The best line of play is to draw two rounds of trumps with the ace and king and then ruff a club in hand. Assuming a favourable trump break, you will still have twelve tricks when the clubs are 3–3 or 4–2. And the precaution of ruffing a club may pay a big dividend when the suit is divided 5–1.

The complete deal:

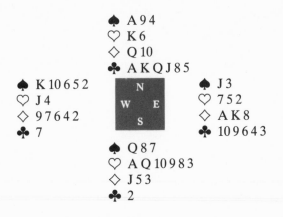

```
              ♠ A 9 4
              ♡ K 6
              ◇ Q 10
              ♣ A K Q J 8 5
♠ K 10 6 5 2                 ♠ J 3
♡ J 4          N             ♡ 7 5 2
◇ 9 7 6 4 2  W   E           ◇ A K 8
♣ 7            S             ♣ 10 9 6 4 3
              ♠ Q 8 7
              ♡ A Q 10 9 8 3
              ◇ J 5 3
              ♣ 2
```

Having started with only two trumps, West is unable to over-ruff on the second round of clubs. After drawing trumps you can enter dummy with the ace of spades and discard four of your five losers on the established clubs.

PROBLEM 14

♠ J 8 6 3
♡ K 8 4
♢ J 10 3
♣ Q 8 7

♠ K Q 5
♡ A J 2
Game all   ♢ A Q 7 6
Dealer South   ♣ K 4 3

The Bidding

SOUTH	WEST	NORTH	EAST
1 ♢	Pass	1 ♠	Pass
3 NT	Pass	Pass	Pass

The Lead

West plays the six of clubs to the seven, ten and king. How do you plan the play?

Review

You can count only four immediate winners, but there are prospects of establishing extra tricks in spades, diamonds and even in clubs. What is the correct line of play?

Solution

Assuming West to have made a normal fourth-highest lead, you can count on making an extra club trick. There can be little chance of success if West holds both of the missing key cards – the ace of spades and the king of diamonds – with his long clubs. But the contract is assured when West has only one of these cards. To get the timing right you must play on diamonds before spades.

Cross to dummy with the king of hearts at trick two and run the jack of diamonds. If West is able to win he may clear the clubs by playing ace and another, but unless he has the ace of spades as well he will be unable to regain the lead to enjoy his long clubs. If the jack of diamonds wins, continue with the ten of diamonds. As long as the key cards are divided you are bound to make nine tricks.

The complete deal:

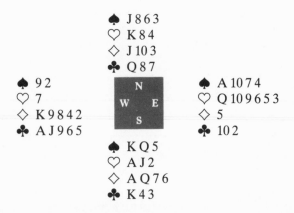

```
              ♠ J 8 6 3
              ♡ K 8 4
              ◇ J 10 3
              ♣ Q 8 7
♠ 9 2              N              ♠ A 10 7 4
♡ 7           W       E          ♡ Q 10 9 6 5 3
◇ K 9 8 4 2        S             ◇ 5
♣ A J 9 6 5                      ♣ 10 2
              ♠ K Q 5
              ♡ A J 2
              ◇ A Q 7 6
              ♣ K 4 3
```

Note that the contract must be defeated if you play a spade at trick two. East wins and clears the clubs, and you can make no more than eight tricks before letting West in to run his clubs.

PROBLEM 15

♠ 5
♡ A K 9 6 4
♢ 8 7 2
♣ 8 7 6 3

♠ A J 7 2
♡ 5 2
♢ A K 10 9 6 5 3
♣ —

Game all
Dealer East

The Bidding

WEST	NORTH	EAST	SOUTH
		1 ♣	Dble
Pass	2 ♡	3 ♣	3 ♢
Pass	4 ♢	Pass	4 ♠
Pass	6 ♢	Pass	Pass
Dble	Pass	Pass	Pass

The Lead

West leads the queen of diamonds on which East discards the ace of clubs. After winning the first trick how do you continue?

Review

This is a little awkward. On any other lead you would have been able to ruff three spades in dummy. Now there appears to be some danger of losing a trump trick and a spade trick. What can you do about it?

Solution

The temptation to start an immediate cross-ruff must be resisted. West is marked with at least four spades since East failed to mention the suit at his second turn, and it is unlikely that you can establish a second spade trick.

The heart suit represents the best chance of a twelfth trick and you have to be careful with the timing. To cater for four hearts with West as well as a 3–3 break, you must tackle the suit at once. After the ace and king of hearts and a heart ruff, you cash the ace of spades and ruff a spade in dummy. Now, if the hearts were 3–3, you ruff a club, ruff another spade, and discard your remaining spade loser on an established heart. If East showed out on the third heart, however, you ruff a fourth heart, ruff a second spade, and play the fifth heart for a discard of your last spade.

The complete deal:

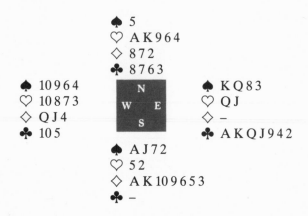

	♠ 5	
	♡ A K 9 6 4	
	◇ 8 7 2	
	♣ 8 7 6 3	
♠ 10 9 6 4		♠ K Q 8 3
♡ 10 8 7 3		♡ Q J
◇ Q J 4		◇ –
♣ 10 5		♣ A K Q J 9 4 2
	♠ A J 7 2	
	♡ 5 2	
	◇ A K 10 9 6 5 3	
	♣ –	

If you ruff a spade before tackling the hearts there is no way to recover.

PROBLEM 16

♠ K Q 10 8
♡ A K 7 4
◇ 9 2
♣ A 5 4

♠ A J 9 4
♡ 10 8
Love all ◇ A Q
Dealer South ♣ K Q 8 7 2

The Bidding

SOUTH	WEST	NORTH	EAST
1 ♣	Pass	1 ♡	Pass
1 ♠	Pass	2 ◇	Pass
3 NT	Pass	4 ♠	Pass
5 ◇	Pass	5 ♡	Pass
6 ♣	Pass	7 ♠	Pass
Pass	Pass		

The Lead

West opts for the traditional lead of a trump against your grand slam. Dummy's eight holds the trick as East follows suit. How do you plan the play?

Review

If both black suits divide 3–2 you can count thirteen tricks. Even if the clubs happen to be 4–1 you can always ruff the fourth club in dummy and fall back on the diamond finesse. Is there anything better?

Solution

Finesses are best avoided in grand slam contracts. Here the best chance comes from a dummy reversal. Provided that two rounds of hearts stand up, you can overcome a 4–1 break in one of the black suits.

Cash the ace and king of hearts and ruff a third heart with the ace of spades. Careful now! Correct timing requires that you re-enter dummy with the ace of clubs. Ruff the last heart and draw trumps, discarding the queen of diamonds from your hand. If the clubs prove to be 4–1, you can ruff out the suit and return to hand with the ace of diamonds to enjoy the long club.

The complete deal:

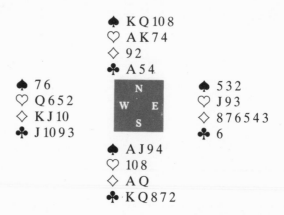

```
              ♠ K Q 10 8
              ♡ A K 7 4
              ◇ 9 2
              ♣ A 5 4
♠ 7 6                              ♠ 5 3 2
♡ Q 6 5 2         N                ♡ J 9 3
◇ K J 10      W       E            ◇ 8 7 6 5 4 3
♣ J 10 9 3        S                ♣ 6
              ♠ A J 9 4
              ♡ 10 8
              ◇ A Q
              ♣ K Q 8 7 2
```

Note the importance of using the club entry to dummy at the first opportunity. If you use a trump entry instead, East will seize the chance to discard his lone club on the fourth round of hearts, and you will have no way of returning to dummy to draw his last trump.

PROBLEM 17

♠ Q 7 2
♡ Q J 10 2
◇ 5 2
♣ A Q 7 4

♠ A 9 6
♡ K 7 4 3
◇ A Q 4
♣ J 10 3

Game all
Dealer South

The Bidding

SOUTH	WEST	NORTH	EAST
1 ♡	Pass	3 ♡	Pass
4 ♡	Pass	Pass	Pass

The Lead

West leads the nine of clubs. How do you plan the play?

Review

There is danger all around. The opening lead suggests that the club finesse is likely to fail, there is a certain loser in trumps and another one in spades, and on top of all that there is the threat of a club ruff. How can you hope to surmount these hurdles?

Solution

The diamond finesse will need to be right for a start. Even then, you cannot afford to suffer a club ruff except in special circumstances whereby West is compelled to return the lost trick in one way or another. A semi-elimination represents the only chance of creating the required conditions, and the timing has to be precise.

Win the ace of clubs, finesse the queen of diamonds, cash the ace and ruff the third diamond on the table. Then play a trump. If West began with the king of spades and doubletons in both trumps and clubs, he will be able to ruff a club but will then have to return a spade or diamond, either of which will serve to dispose of your spade loser.

The complete deal:

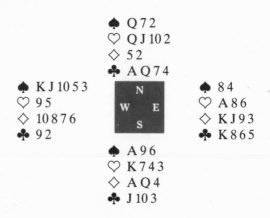

It is not good enough to play low from dummy at trick one. On winning the club king East will return not a club but a spade. If you go up with the ace, East will eventually score a spade ruff, while if you play low West will win and switch back to clubs, thereby making sure of his club ruff.

PROBLEM 18

♠ Q 9 8
♡ K Q 2
◇ K Q 6 5
♣ Q 7 3

```
      N
  W       E
      S
```

♠ K 6 5 4
♡ 6
Game all   ◇ A 7 4 2
Dealer West   ♣ A J 10 2

The Bidding

WEST	NORTH	EAST	SOUTH
Pass	1◇	Pass	1♠
Pass	1NT	Pass	3♣
Pass	3♠	Pass	4◇
Pass	4♠	Pass	Pass
Pass			

The Lead

West leads the four of hearts to the queen and ace. East continues with the jack of hearts which you ruff in hand, West following with the three. How do you plan the play?

Review

The trump suit is far from robust. Clearly you must hope to find the trumps 3–3, and you also need the king of clubs onside. What is the best way to tackle the hand?

Solution

Playing in a 4–3 trump fit is a hazardous business. You are likely to lose control unless you can force out the ace of spades on the first round of the suit. Where is the trump ace most likely to be lurking? East has already shown up with the ace and jack of hearts and you are placing him with the king of clubs. With the ace of spades as well he might have made himself heard in the bidding. So it is West you must play for the ace of spades, and correct timing requires the play of the king of spades at trick three.

When West takes his ace and knocks out the king of hearts, you can discard a diamond from hand and continue with a low trump from both hands. The remaining small trump in your hand protects against a further heart lead, and if the trumps and the clubs are favourable you will lose only two spades and one heart.

The complete deal:

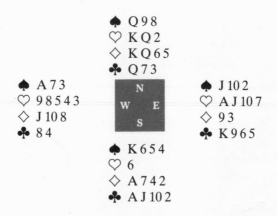

```
              ♠ Q 9 8
              ♡ K Q 2
              ♢ K Q 6 5
              ♣ Q 7 3
  ♠ A 7 3          N          ♠ J 10 2
  ♡ 9 8 5 4 3   W     E       ♡ A J 10 7
  ♢ J 10 8         S          ♢ 9 3
  ♣ 8 4                       ♣ K 9 6 5
              ♠ K 6 5 4
              ♡ 6
              ♢ A 7 4 2
              ♣ A J 10 2
```

The timing of the trump play is all-important on this hand. There is no means of recovery if you play a low trump to the queen at trick three.

PROBLEM 19

♠ K 10 6 3
♡ –
♢ A J 10 8 7
♣ 10 9 8 3

♠ A 5
♡ K 7 6 5
♢ 2
♣ K Q J 7 4 2

Game all
Dealer South

The Bidding

SOUTH	WEST	NORTH	EAST
1 ♣	Pass	1 ♢	Pass
1 ♡	Pass	1 ♠	Pass
3 ♣	Pass	5 ♣	Pass
6 ♣	Pass	Pass	Pass

The Lead

West leads the five of clubs against your slam. East takes the ace and returns the two of spades which you win with the ace. How should you continue?

Review

It is perhaps fortunate that East could not find a second trump to return. Even so, you can count no more than eleven tricks on a cross-ruff. Where is the twelfth trick to come from?

Solution

Clearly you must set up a long diamond as the twelfth trick and there is a strong temptation to play a diamond to the ace immediately. If you go through the correct procedure of playing the hand over in your mind, however, you may realise that this will establish the diamond winner too early. A diamond to the ace, diamond ruff, heart ruff, diamond ruff, heart ruff, diamond ruff. Assuming the 4–3 diamond break that you need, the long diamond will now be established, but you still need to ruff another heart in dummy and the timing is hopelessly wrong. After ruffing the heart you have no way of returning to hand to draw the last trump before enjoying your second diamond trick.

Correct timing requires the ruff of a heart at trick three. Then the ace of diamonds, diamond ruff, heart ruff, diamond ruff, heart ruff, diamond ruff. Now you can draw the last trump, cross to the king of spades, and discard your last heart on the established diamond.

The complete deal:

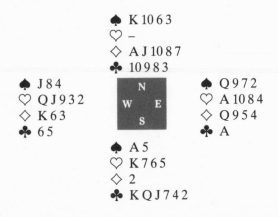

```
                    ♠ K 10 6 3
                    ♡ –
                    ♢ A J 10 8 7
                    ♣ 10 9 8 3
    ♠ J 8 4              N          ♠ Q 9 7 2
    ♡ Q J 9 3 2      W      E       ♡ A 10 8 4
    ♢ K 6 3              S          ♢ Q 9 5 4
    ♣ 6 5                           ♣ A
                    ♠ A 5
                    ♡ K 7 6 5
                    ♢ 2
                    ♣ K Q J 7 4 2
```

PROBLEM 20

♠ 83
♡ 10 6 3
♦ Q J 8 6 5 2
♣ 7 5

♠ Q J 9
♡ A Q 8 7 2
♦ A 4
♣ A 8 3

Love all
Dealer South

The Bidding

SOUTH	WEST	NORTH	EAST
1 ♡	2 ♣	Pass	Pass
2 ♡	Pass	Pass	2 NT
Pass	Pass	3 ♡	Pass
Pass	Pass		

The Lead

West attacks with the king of clubs and continues with the queen. East plays low-high and you take your ace on the second round. You ruff the third club with the three of hearts and East follows suit. How should you continue?

Review

On the bidding the finesses in the red suits are likely to be right, but there is a lot of work to do on the hand. What is the best sequence of plays?

Solution

It can hardly be right to take an immediate trump finesse, for you would never get back to dummy. An alternative is to run the queen of diamonds at trick four. If East refuses to cover you can switch to spades, finessing the nine and eventually ruffing the third spade in dummy to gain access for a trump finesse. There is a hidden danger in this line, however. On winning the first spade West could play a second diamond, preparing the ground for a trump promotion when his partner gains the lead on the next round of spades.

The contract is not likely to succeed unless the ten of spades is with East, and the right play is a spade to your nine at trick four. If West switches to a trump you may be able to avoid a trump loser altogether, while if West returns anything else you can expect to ruff the third spade on the table and finesse first in diamonds and then in hearts to bring in nine tricks.

The complete deal:

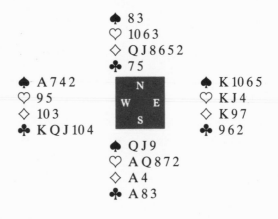

```
                    ♠ 8 3
                    ♡ 10 6 3
                    ◇ Q J 8 6 5 2
                    ♣ 7 5
    ♠ A 7 4 2            N            ♠ K 10 6 5
    ♡ 9 5            W       E        ♡ K J 4
    ◇ 10 3              S             ◇ K 9 7
    ♣ K Q J 10 4                      ♣ 9 6 2
                    ♠ Q J 9
                    ♡ A Q 8 7 2
                    ◇ A 4
                    ♣ A 8 3
```

PROBLEM 21

♠ K J 5
♡ 7 6 2
◇ A 8 6 3
♣ A Q 5

```
    N
 W     E
    S
```

♠ Q 10 2
♡ K Q 4
◇ K Q 7
♣ J 7 4 3

Love all
Dealer North

The Bidding

WEST	NORTH	EAST	SOUTH
	1 ◇	1 ♡	3 NT
Pass	Pass	Pass	

The Lead

West leads the nine of hearts to the ten and king. How do you plan the play?

Review

You appear to have plenty of winners – two tricks in each major suit, at least three diamonds and two clubs. It is just a matter of collecting your nine winners without giving the defenders a chance to score five tricks first. What is the correct sequence of plays?

Solution

On such hands the secret of success is to test all the possibilities in logical order. If East has two entries in the black suits you are not going to succeed unless the diamonds are 3–3. So the first priority must be to find out how the diamonds are behaving. Play the seven of diamonds to dummy's ace at trick two and continue with a second diamond to your king. If both opponents follow you can safely cash the third diamond. If the suit proves to be 3–3, you have enough tricks without developing the clubs. Just knock out the ace of spades and run for home with two spades, two hearts, four diamonds and a club.

When someone shows out on the second or third round of diamonds you need extra tricks from the clubs, and you are providently in the right hand to take the club finesse. Now you have to bank on East's holding only one entry in the black suits. If he has the king of clubs, he may set up his hearts but will have no entry to cash them. If East's entry is the ace of spades the club finesse will succeed, whereupon you can drive out the ace of spades and make sure of your nine tricks.

The complete deal:

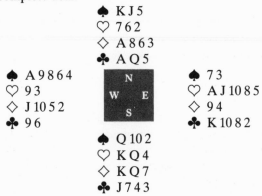

<pre>
                    ♠ K J 5
                    ♡ 7 6 2
                    ♢ A 8 6 3
                    ♣ A Q 5
    ♠ A 9 8 6 4   ♠ 7 3
    ♡ 9 3   ♡ A J 10 8 5
    ♢ J 10 5 2   ♢ 9 4
    ♣ 9 6   ♣ K 10 8 2
                    ♠ Q 10 2
                    ♡ K Q 4
                    ♢ K Q 7
                    ♣ J 7 4 3
</pre>

PROBLEM 22

♠ 4
♡ K J 3
♢ A Q 9 6 4
♣ Q J 6 3

```
      N
   W     E
      S
```

♠ A
♡ A Q 10 6 5 2
Love all   ♢ J 3
Dealer South   ♣ A 8 7 2

The Bidding

SOUTH	WEST	NORTH	EAST
1 ♡	3 ♠	4 ♡	4 ♠
5 ♣	Pass	5 ♢	Pass
6 ♡	Pass	Pass	Pass

The Lead

West leads the queen of spades to your ace. How do you plan the play?

Review

You have reached a sound slam where the only problem is to avoid the loss of a trick in each minor suit. What is the correct sequence of plays?

Solution

A successful diamond finesse would see you home, for you should then lose no more than one trick in clubs. The picture is not so bright if the jack of diamonds loses to the king, however. East will no doubt return a club whether he has the king or not, and you will have to make an immediate decision on whether to risk the finesse or whether to bank on bringing down the ten of diamonds.

It is usually a mistake to place yourself in a position where the opponents can restrict your options in this way. The best line of play is to enter dummy with the jack of hearts at trick two and play a low diamond towards your jack. If East has the diamond king your troubles are over. And if West is able to capture the jack with the king, at least he cannot put you to a guess in clubs before you know how the diamonds are behaving.

The complete deal:

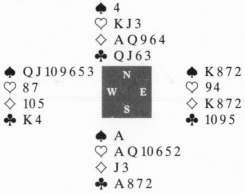

```
                    ♠ 4
                    ♡ K J 3
                    ♢ A Q 9 6 4
                    ♣ Q J 6 3
♠ Q J 10 9 6 5 3        N          ♠ K 8 7 2
♡ 8 7               W       E      ♡ 9 4
♢ 10 5                             ♢ K 8 7 2
♣ K 4                  S          ♣ 10 9 5
                    ♠ A
                    ♡ A Q 10 6 5 2
                    ♢ J 3
                    ♣ A 8 7 2
```

PROBLEM 23

```
                    ♠ K Q J 10
                    ♡ 7 3
                    ◇ K 4 2
                    ♣ 8 7 5 2
                    ┌─────────┐
                    │    N    │
                    │  W   E  │
                    │    S    │
                    └─────────┘
                    ♠ 4 3
                    ♡ A Q 6 2
Love all            ◇ Q 8 7 6
Dealer East         ♣ A 9 6
```

The Bidding

WEST	NORTH	EAST	SOUTH
		1 ◇	Pass
Pass	1 ♠	Dble	1 NT
Pass	Pass	Pass	

The Lead

West leads the ten of hearts to his partner's king. You allow this to win and East continues with the jack of hearts to your ace. When you play a spade to the ten both defenders play low, as expected. How should you continue?

Review

The situation does not look too good and you are perhaps wishing you had passed the double of one spade. Prospects of making seven tricks in no trumps are not great, but at least you escaped the initial diamond lead that would have given you no chance at all. How can you arrange to make some more spade tricks?

Solution

The only chance is to organise some sort of end-play against East, and for this to work you must cut communications between the defenders. The best shot is to play a club and duck it at trick four. You can win a heart or diamond return in hand, cash any remaining winners in hearts and clubs, and exit with a spade or a club, hoping that East will have to win. After cashing his remaining club winners East will then have to lead a spade or a diamond, giving you access to dummy.

The complete deal:

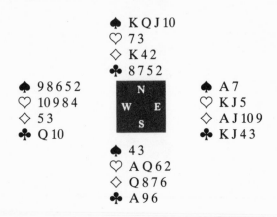

```
                    ♠ K Q J 10
                    ♡ 7 3
                    ◇ K 4 2
                    ♣ 8 7 5 2
  ♠ 9 8 6 5 2                      ♠ A 7
  ♡ 10 9 8 4         N            ♡ K J 5
  ◇ 5 3           W     E          ◇ A J 10 9
  ♣ Q 10            S             ♣ K J 4 3
                    ♠ 4 3
                    ♡ A Q 6 2
                    ◇ Q 8 7 6
                    ♣ A 9 6
```

As East remarks pointedly, there is a lot to be said for leading partner's suit. If West had led a diamond you would have had no chance of making more than five tricks.

PROBLEM 24

```
            ♠ A 7 6 3
            ♡ 8 5 4
            ◇ K 7 4
            ♣ A J 5

              N
           W     E
              S

            ♠ K Q 10 9 4
            ♡ K 7
Love all     ◇ A 5 2
Dealer West  ♣ Q 6 2
```

The Bidding

WEST	NORTH	EAST	SOUTH
1 NT*	Pass	2 ♡	2 ♠
Pass	4 ♠	Pass	Pass
Pass			

*12–14

The Lead

West leads the queen of diamonds. How do you plan the play?

Review

You appear to have exactly nine tricks – five trumps, two diamonds and two clubs. There is no chance of finding the ace of hearts favourably placed since the opening bid marks the missing high cards with West. If the trumps break no worse than 3–1, however, you may be able to arrange an end-play against West, throwing him in and forcing a favourable return. Are there any snags to look out for?

Solution

You must guard against allowing East to gain the lead, for a heart lead through your king would spell defeat. The only way East might gain the lead is on the third round of diamonds. To protect against the possibility of East holding the ten of diamonds, therefore, you should allow West to win the first trick with the diamond queen. You can win the next diamond with the king, draw trumps, cash the ace of diamonds and finesse the jack of clubs. The ace of clubs comes next, and if the king does not drop you can throw West in with the third round of clubs, forcing him either to open up the hearts or to concede a ruff and discard.

The complete deal:

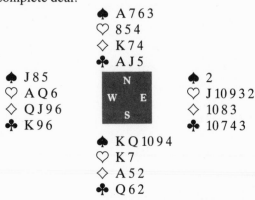

```
                  ♠ A 7 6 3
                  ♡ 8 5 4
                  ◇ K 7 4
                  ♣ A J 5
    ♠ J 8 5            N            ♠ 2
    ♡ A Q 6       W         E       ♡ J 10 9 3 2
    ◇ Q J 9 6          S           ◇ 10 8 3
    ♣ K 9 6                        ♣ 10 7 4 3
                  ♠ K Q 10 9 4
                  ♡ K 7
                  ◇ A 5 2
                  ♣ Q 6 2
```

Careful defence will always defeat the contract if you win the first diamond.

PROBLEM 25

♠ 4
♡ A K 7 6 5
◇ A K 5 4 2
♣ 6 4

♠ K 5 3 2
♡ Q
◇ 10 9 8 6
♣ K Q 10 5

Game all
Dealer North

The Bidding

WEST	NORTH	EAST	SOUTH
	1 ♡	Pass	1 ♠
Pass	2 ◇	Pass	2 NT
Pass	3 NT	Pass	Pass
Pass			

The Lead

West leads the seven of spades to the queen and king. How do you continue?

Review

West must have a powerful reason for leading your suit, so it seems advisable to give up all idea of snatching a ninth trick in clubs. Concentrating your attention on the red suits, you note that three hearts and five diamonds will see you home. How are you going to manage the entries?

Solution

There could be trouble in the diamond suit since dummy's small cards are such midgets. There is bound to be a blockage even if the suit divides 2–2. The difficulty might be overcome by cashing the queen of hearts at trick two. You could then discard the blocking diamonds in your hand on the ace and king of hearts.

Is there an alternative? If East drops an honour on the first round of diamonds, it would be reasonable to regard this as a singleton according to the principle of free choice. Might you not then wish to be able to return to hand with the queen of hearts and run a diamond through West on the second round? No, it won't work, for West will cover the second diamond and his seven will be high enough to prevent you from unblocking on the hearts.

You have to play for 2–2 diamonds in that case, and it is correct to play the queen of hearts at trick two.

The complete deal:

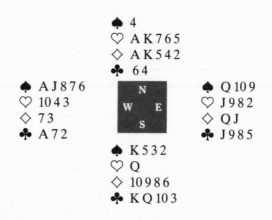

```
                    ♠ 4
                    ♡ A K 7 6 5
                    ◇ A K 5 4 2
                    ♣ 6 4
    ♠ A J 8 7 6                       ♠ Q 10 9
    ♡ 10 4 3          N               ♡ J 9 8 2
    ◇ 7 3         W       E           ◇ Q J
    ♣ A 7 2          S               ♣ J 9 8 5
                    ♠ K 5 3 2
                    ♡ Q
                    ◇ 10 9 8 6
                    ♣ K Q 10 3
```

PROBLEM 26

♠ 6 2
♡ J 7 5 2
♢ 6
♣ A J 10 6 4 3

```
    N
 W     E
    S
```

♠ A 9
♡ A K Q 6
♢ A J 9 7 5 2
♣ K

Game all
Dealer South

The Bidding

SOUTH	WEST	NORTH	EAST
2 ♣	Pass	3 ♣	Pass
3 ♢	Pass	4 ♣	Pass
4 ♡	Pass	5 ♡	Pass
5 ♠	Pass	6 ♡	Pass
Pass	Pass		

The Lead

West leads the king of spades to your ace. How do you plan the play?

Review

It is a fairly thin slam, but your losing spade can go on the ace of clubs and there is no reason why you should not be able to bring in the diamond suit. What is the correct sequence of plays?

Solution

You may feel a strong urge to unblock the king of clubs at trick two, but temptation must sometimes be resisted. Your hand is not so rich in entries that you can afford to be wasteful, and there is no urgency about the spade discard. The right move is to cash the ace of diamonds and ruff a second diamond in dummy. Now return to the king of clubs and play a third diamond. If West follows suit, ruff high in dummy, discard your spade on the ace of clubs and play on trumps, hoping for at least one of the red suits to break evenly.

If West ruffs the third diamond, you can over-ruff, take your discard on the ace of clubs, draw trumps and concede a diamond.

The complete deal:

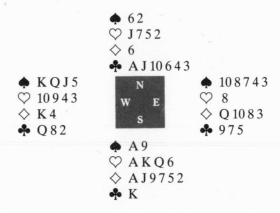

```
              ♠ 6 2
              ♡ J 7 5 2
              ♢ 6
              ♣ A J 10 6 4 3
♠ K Q J 5                      ♠ 10 8 7 4 3
♡ 10 9 4 3      N              ♡ 8
♢ K 4        W   E             ♢ Q 10 8 3
♣ Q 8 2          S             ♣ 9 7 5
              ♠ A 9
              ♡ A K Q 6
              ♢ A J 9 7 5 2
              ♣ K
```

In practice West may discard a spade or a club on the third diamond but this causes no great problem. You ruff low, take your discard on the club ace, ruff a spade and play another diamond. This time West cannot ruff without allowing you to make all thirteen tricks, so he discards again and you make all eight of your trumps separately.

Note that the contract cannot be made if you are careless enough to cash the king of clubs at trick two.

PROBLEM 27

♠ A 7 4 3
♡ 9 5 4
♢ A 6 5
♣ A 4 3

```
        N
    W       E
        S
```

♠ 6
♡ A Q
♢ K 9 3
♣ K Q J 10 7 6 5

Game all
Dealer South

The Bidding

SOUTH	WEST	NORTH	EAST
1 ♣	1 ♠	2 ♠	Pass
4 ♣	Pass	4 ♠	Pass
4 NT	Pass	5 ♠	Pass
5 NT	Pass	6 ♣	Pass
Pass	Pass		

The Lead

West leads the king of spades to dummy's ace. You ruff a spade, cash the king of clubs and continue with a club to the ace. West discards a spade on the second club, and when you ruff another spade East follows with the ten. How should you continue?

Review

Although there are only eleven top tricks, you should be able to score a twelfth through a throw-in against West, who is likely to have the king of hearts. What is the best way of implementing the throw-in?

Solution

It is tempting to complete the elimination of the spades by crossing to the ace of diamonds and ruffing the last spade. The king and another diamond would come next, and West may have to open up the hearts or concede a ruff and discard. Unfortunately there is no guarantee that West will have all the diamond honours. If East has one of them – even the ten – West may escape the throw-in by unblocking in diamonds.

There is a stronger line of play that will always succeed when West holds the king of hearts. Leave the last spade in dummy and run the rest of the trumps. In order to keep his master spade and the guarded king of hearts, West will have to reduce to two cards in diamonds. The play of the king and ace of diamonds will extract these cards, and there is no escape from the throw-in when you play the fourth spade from dummy and discard the losing diamond from your hand.

The complete deal:

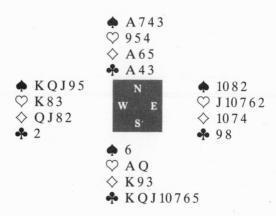

```
                 ♠ A 7 4 3
                 ♡ 9 5 4
                 ♢ A 6 5
                 ♣ A 4 3
  ♠ K Q J 9 5        N        ♠ 10 8 2
  ♡ K 8 3         W     E     ♡ J 10 7 6 2
  ♢ Q J 8 2          S        ♢ 10 7 4
  ♣ 2                          ♣ 9 8
                 ♠ 6
                 ♡ A Q
                 ♢ K 9 3
                 ♣ K Q J 10 7 6 5
```

PROBLEM 28

```
              ♠ K
              ♡ 10 7 6
              ◇ A J 8
              ♣ A Q J 9 6 3

                  ┌─────────┐
                  │    N    │
                  │ W     E │
                  │    S    │
                  └─────────┘

              ♠ Q 10 9 8 7 6 2
              ♡ A J 9
Game all      ◇ 3
Dealer South  ♣ K 5
```

The Bidding

SOUTH	WEST	NORTH	EAST
1 ♠	3 ◇*	3 NT	Pass
4 ♠	Pass	Pass	Pass

Weak jump overcall

The Lead

West leads the seven of clubs. How do you plan the play?

Review

Once trumps have been drawn you should be able to discard the heart losers on the long clubs. Is there any reason to suspect that this play may not work?

Solution

The warning bell should be sounding in your ear, for the seven of clubs looks very much like a singleton. Suppose you win the first trick in hand and play a spade to the king. East is likely to have the ace, and after taking it he will give his partner a club ruff. A diamond switch will inevitably follow, removing your last entry to dummy and forcing you either to continue clubs, relying on West having no more than two trumps, or play a heart, banking on East having both honours.

You might get away with it, but it is surely better to rely on the double heart finesse. Win the first trick in dummy and play a heart for a finesse of the nine. West may win and knock out the ace of diamonds, but you can take a second heart finesse before playing on trumps. As long as East has one of the heart honours you should be all right, for you can afford to lose one heart and two spades. You will go down only if West has a small doubleton spade and is able to score a ruff.

The complete deal:

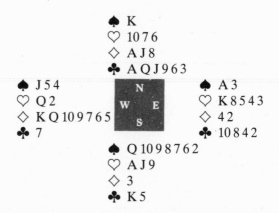

```
              ♠ K
              ♡ 10 7 6
              ◇ A J 8
              ♣ A Q J 9 6 3
♠ J 5 4                        ♠ A 3
♡ Q 2            N             ♡ K 8 5 4 3
◇ K Q 10 9 7 6 5  W   E        ◇ 4 2
♣ 7               S            ♣ 10 8 4 2
              ♠ Q 10 9 8 7 6 2
              ♡ A J 9
              ◇ 3
              ♣ K 5
```

PROBLEM 29

♠ A J 9 3
♡ 7
◇ A 8 7 5 2
♣ A K 10

```
        N
    W       E
        S
```

♠ 6 5
♡ A Q 9
◇ 6
♣ Q J 9 8 7 5 2

Game all
Dealer South

The Bidding

SOUTH	WEST	NORTH	EAST
3 ♣	Pass	3 ◇	Pass
3 ♡	Pass	4 ♣	Pass
4 ◇	Pass	7 ♣	Pass
Pass	Pass		

The Lead

West leads the eight of spades to dummy's ace. How do you plan the play?

Review

Partner has some fine cards but he seems to have pressed rather hard in the bidding. Counting two ruffs in dummy, your total comes to no more than twelve tricks. It looks as though you will have to establish a long diamond to take care of your losing spade. What is the correct sequence of plays?

Solution

The opening lead has awkwardly removed your only side entry to dummy. If you cash the diamond ace at trick two, planning to ruff three diamonds in hand and two hearts in dummy, you may establish a long diamond but you will never be able to enjoy it. One defender will be left with an undrawn trump and you will be held to twelve tricks.

You need 4–3 diamonds and 2–1 trumps, to be sure, but you also need a little more. Since two of dummy's trumps are required for drawing the enemy trumps, you can afford to ruff only *one* heart on the table. This means that you have to rely on East's holding the king of hearts. The correct play at trick two is a heart for a finesse of the queen. If this succeeds, you can continue with a diamond to the ace, a diamond ruff, a club to the ace, a diamond ruff, a club to the king and a further diamond ruff. Now you simply ruff the nine of hearts on the table and discard the losing spade on the established diamond.

The complete deal:

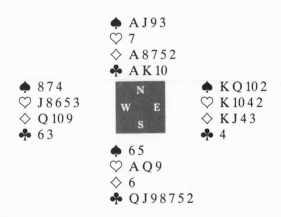

```
                ♠ A J 9 3
                ♡ 7
                ♢ A 8 7 5 2
                ♣ A K 10
  ♠ 8 7 4          N         ♠ K Q 10 2
  ♡ J 8 6 5 3   W     E      ♡ K 10 4 2
  ♢ Q 10 9        S         ♢ K J 4 3
  ♣ 6 3                      ♣ 4
                ♠ 6 5
                ♡ A Q 9
                ♢ 6
                ♣ Q J 9 8 7 5 2
```

The contract cannot be made if the ace of diamonds is played at trick two. Note that the traditional lead of a trump would have given you an easy ride on this occasion.

PROBLEM 30

♠ K Q 3
♡ J 5 4 3
♦ 10 7 6 4
♣ Q 7

```
        N
    W       E
        S
```

♠ 7 5
♡ A K Q 8 7
♦ A Q J 9
♣ J 9

Game all
Dealer South

The Bidding

SOUTH	WEST	NORTH	EAST
1 ♡	Pass	2 ♡	Pass
4 ♡	Pass	Pass	Pass

The Lead

West cashes the ace and king of clubs and switches to the nine of spades. East captures the queen with his ace and returns the jack of spades to dummy's king. How do you plan the play?

Review

Needing the rest of the tricks, you must hope for the diamond finesse to be right. It seems natural to draw trumps, ending in dummy, and then run the ten of diamonds. Is there any objection to this line of play?

Solution

Drawing trumps immediately does not cater for the possibility of a 4–1 diamond break. Suppose the ten of diamonds wins and you continue with a diamond to the jack. If West shows out on the second round you will be in trouble, desperate to enter dummy for a further finesse but unable to do so for lack of a second trump entry.

The difficulty is overcome by better timing. You should take a diamond finesse before touching trumps, playing a low card to your jack. When this wins you can continue with high trumps from hand. Enter dummy with the heart jack on the third round (or on the fourth round if the trumps happen to break 4–0) and run the ten of diamonds for a second finesse. Now you are in a position to take a further finesse in diamonds if it proves necessary.

The complete deal:

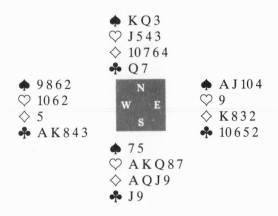

```
                    ♠ K Q 3
                    ♡ J 5 4 3
                    ◇ 10 7 6 4
                    ♣ Q 7
   ♠ 9 8 6 2          N          ♠ A J 10 4
   ♡ 10 6 2       W     E        ♡ 9
   ◇ 5              S            ◇ K 8 3 2
   ♣ A K 8 4 3                   ♣ 10 6 5 2
                    ♠ 7 5
                    ♡ A K Q 8 7
                    ◇ A Q J 9
                    ♣ J 9
```

Note that the contract must fail if the ten of diamonds is played from dummy, or the nine from hand, at trick four.

PROBLEM 31

♠ A K Q
♡ K Q 4
◇ K Q 2
♣ A 9 7 4

♠ J 9 5
♡ A 10 2
◇ 8 7 6 4 3
♣ K Q

Love all
Dealer North

The Bidding

WEST	NORTH	EAST	SOUTH
	2 ♣	Pass	2 NT
Pass	3 NT	Pass	6 NT
Pass	Pass	Pass	

The Lead

West leads the nine of hearts against your slam. How do you plan the play?

Review

You can count three winners in each major suit and three in clubs. It looks as though you need to bring in the diamond suit, playing twice through West and hoping to find him with the ace. Are there any particular snags to look out for?

Solution

Suppose you play low from dummy and the jack of hearts forces your ace. West will no doubt play a low diamond at trick two, and after winning in dummy you will have to return to hand with a club to play another diamond. Now West will be in a position to jam your communications by rising with the ace of diamonds and returning a club, taking out your last entry before the diamonds are unblocked. You will thus be held to two diamond tricks and forced to pray for a miracle in clubs.

There is no need to allow the defenders to mess you about like this. It is just a matter of timing your entries sensibly. Win the first trick in dummy with the king or queen of hearts, cross to hand with the queen of clubs and play a diamond. When West plays low and dummy wins, play a club to your king and continue diamonds. There is nothing West can do since your heart entry is immune from attack. You can win the heart switch in dummy, unblock the diamonds, and finally make use of the heart ace to enjoy the established diamonds.

The complete deal:

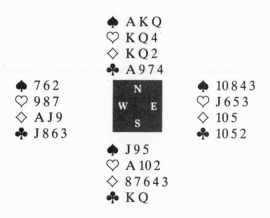

```
              ♠ A K Q
              ♡ K Q 4
              ◇ K Q 2
              ♣ A 9 7 4
  ♠ 7 6 2        N        ♠ 10 8 4 3
  ♡ 9 8 7     W     E     ♡ J 6 5 3
  ◇ A J 9        S        ◇ 10 5
  ♣ J 8 6 3               ♣ 10 5 2
              ♠ J 9 5
              ♡ A 10 2
              ◇ 8 7 6 4 3
              ♣ K Q
```

PROBLEM 32

♠ K Q J 10 7 3
♡ 4
♢ K 10 7 2
♣ A Q

```
      N
  W       E
      S
```

♠ A
♡ A J 9 6 3
♢ A J 9 3
♣ 7 5 4

Game all
Dealer North

The Bidding

WEST	NORTH	EAST	SOUTH
Pass	1 ♠	Pass	2 ♡
Pass	3 ♠	Pass	4 ♢
Pass	5 ♣	Pass	5 ♠
Pass	6 ♢	Pass	Pass
Pass			

The Lead

West leads the jack of clubs to dummy's ace. Both defenders follow with low cards when you play a diamond to the ace and also when you cash the ace of spades. How do you continue?

Review

You can afford a trump loser provided that you can avoid losing a trick in the side suits, and there must be a good chance of discarding your losing clubs on dummy's spades. Are there any special precautions that need to be taken?

[71]

Solution

Naturally you have no intention of finessing in diamonds. The plan is to play a diamond to the king and then, if the queen does not drop, revert to spades. You hope that the defender with the master diamond will have at least two spades, which will allow you to dispose of your club losers.

But you ought to give a moment's thought to the possibility of a 4–1 trump break. If West has four trumps you are bound to be defeated after a diamond to the king, but if East has the trump length there may be a chance. You will be in a position to use the spades as reserve-trumps, ramming the suit through East. When he ruffs, you can over-ruff, ruff a heart in dummy, and continue spades. However, you must make sure that East is given no chance to ruff your ace of hearts at a later stage. The way to do that is to cash the heart ace before playing a diamond to the king.

The complete deal:

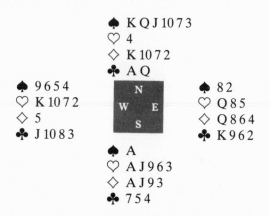

```
                    ♠ K Q J 10 7 3
                    ♡ 4
                    ♢ K 10 7 2
                    ♣ A Q
  ♠ 9 6 5 4              N              ♠ 8 2
  ♡ K 10 7 2        W       E          ♡ Q 8 5
  ♢ 5                    S             ♢ Q 8 6 4
  ♣ J 10 8 3                           ♣ K 9 6 2
                    ♠ A
                    ♡ A J 9 6 3
                    ♢ A J 9 3
                    ♣ 7 5 4
```

The slam cannot be made unless you cash the ace of hearts at trick four. East will simply discard hearts on the spades and wait for his chance, and if you play a heart he will score his small trump by ruffing. If you play a trump he will win and return the suit, leaving you a trick short.

PROBLEM 33

♠ 7 5
♡ Q J 10
♢ K 8 6 5
♣ J 10 7 3

```
      N
  W       E
      S
```

♠ A K 6 2
♡ A K 7 6 4 3
♢ A 4
♣ 6

Game all
Dealer South

The Bidding

SOUTH	WEST	NORTH	EAST
2 ♣	Pass	2 ♢	Pass
2 ♡	Pass	4 ♡	Pass
6 ♡	Pass	Pass	Pass

The Lead

West leads the queen of spades, East follows with the nine and you win with the ace. How do you plan the play?

Review

You seem to have landed in a reasonable slam, and with any luck your only loser will be a club. Needing to ruff two spades in dummy, you must assume that East has at least one spade left. Are there any particular hazards to guard against?

Solution

There is always the possibility of a bad trump break. If someone has four trumps, you will succeed in avoiding a trump loser only if you can score three of your small trumps by ruffing. Every available entry to dummy will be needed for this partial cross-ruff, and you cannot afford to start by ruffing a spade.

Accurate timing requires that you clear your communications by conceding the club loser at trick two. You can win the trump return on the table (or play a trump to dummy yourself after a plain suit return). If someone is void in trumps, you continue with a club ruff, the king of spades, ace and king of diamonds and another club ruff. A spade ruff is followed by a club or a diamond ruff, and all that remains is to ruff the last spade in dummy.

The complete deal:

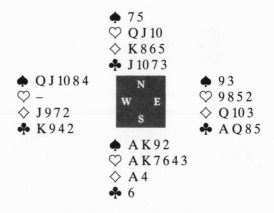

```
                ♠ 7 5
                ♡ Q J 10
                ◇ K 8 6 5
                ♣ J 10 7 3
  ♠ Q J 10 8 4         N         ♠ 9 3
  ♡ –              W       E      ♡ 9 8 5 2
  ◇ J 9 7 2            S          ◇ Q 10 3
  ♣ K 9 4 2                       ♣ A Q 8 5
                ♠ A K 9 2
                ♡ A K 7 6 4 3
                ◇ A 4
                ♣ 6
```

The contract cannot be made unless the club is conceded at an early stage.

PROBLEM 34

♠ 5
♡ 6 2
◇ 10 9 7 4 3
♣ K 9 8 4 2

♠ Q J 10 9 8 4
♡ A Q 10
◇ A
♣ A 10 5

N–S game
Dealer West

The Bidding

WEST	NORTH	EAST	SOUTH
1 ♡	Pass	1 NT	Dble
2 ♡	Pass	Pass	4 ♠
Pass	Pass	Pass	

The Lead

West starts with the ace and king of spades and switches to the jack of clubs. You discard a diamond from dummy on the second spade and win the club switch in hand with the ace. West discards hearts on the next two trumps while you throw a further diamond and a heart from the table. How should you continue?

Review

Your bold bidding will pay off if the clubs are 3–2. You just duck the second round of clubs, and your heart losers eventually disappear on the long clubs. Is there anything to be done if it proves impossible to score four club tricks?

Solution

If the clubs are 4–1, as seems quite likely, East will refuse to take his queen on the second round, thereby holding you to three club tricks. The tenth trick will then have to come from hearts, but there can be no end-play against West unless his exit cards in diamonds are first extracted.

West is likely to have four diamonds but it should be possible to extract them if the timing is precise. Cash the ace of diamonds and continue with the five of clubs. If West discards (another heart, no doubt), insert the eight of clubs from dummy. East must play low to deny you four club tricks, and you use this extra entry to ruff a diamond. Now play the ten of clubs to dummy's king. Having discarded three hearts already, West has to part with a diamond this time. Another diamond ruff draws the last cards in the suit and the play of the queen of hearts puts West on lead, forcing him to yield the last two tricks to your hearts.

The complete deal:

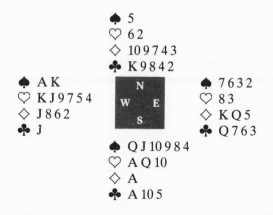

The contract cannot be made if you fail to unblock the ace of diamonds or if you carelessly run the ten of clubs on the second round of the suit.

PROBLEM 35

♠ K 9 5
♡ A K 10 5 3 2
♢ A 6
♣ Q 9

♠ A 6 3
♡ 7 6
E–W game ♢ K Q 10 4
Dealer West ♣ A K 4 3

The Bidding

WEST	NORTH	EAST	SOUTH
Pass	1 ♡	Pass	2 ♣
Pass	3 ♡	Pass	4 NT
Pass	5 ♡	Pass	5 NT
Pass	6 ♡	Pass	7 NT
Pass	Pass	Pass	

The Lead

West leads the seven of diamonds to the six, three and ten. How do you plan the play?

Review

No doubt you are regretting having pressed quite so hard in the bidding. In spite of the favourable lead only eleven tricks are in sight. How do you propose to increase the total to thirteen?

Solution

It looks as though you will have to take the double finesse in hearts, hoping for both honours with West and a 3–2 break. It is not a very good chance and there is no need to rush matters. It cannot hurt to find out a little more about the hand, for the heart finesse will still be available at a later stage. The correct play is a diamond back to the ace at trick two.

The complete deal:

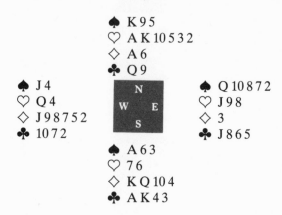

♠ K 9 5
♡ A K 10 5 3 2
♢ A 6
♣ Q 9

♠ J 4
♡ Q 4
♢ J 9 8 7 5 2
♣ 10 7 2

♠ Q 10 8 7 2
♡ J 9 8
♢ 3
♣ J 8 6 5

♠ A 6 3
♡ 7 6
♢ K Q 10 4
♣ A K 4 3

When East discards a spade on the second diamond, an intriguing new possibility opens up. You continue with three rounds of clubs, discarding a heart from the table, and then two more diamonds, discarding a heart and a spade. It soon becomes abundantly clear that East is in the grip of a repeating triple squeeze, and thirteen tricks roll in almost without effort on your part.

West had a difficult choice of opening lead on this hand. Any card except a diamond would have produced a happier result for the defence.

PROBLEM 36

$\spadesuit$ 8752
$\heartsuit$ A 8 3
$\diamondsuit$ A 10 3
$\clubsuit$ A 9 6

$\spadesuit$ A Q J 10 3
$\heartsuit$ 5

Love all $\diamondsuit$ Q J 8 4
Dealer South $\clubsuit$ J 10 3

The Bidding

SOUTH	WEST	NORTH	EAST
1 $\spadesuit$	Pass	3 $\spadesuit$	Pass
4 $\spadesuit$	Pass	Pass	Pass

The Lead

West leads the seven of clubs. When you play low from dummy East wins with the queen and returns the ten of hearts to dummy's ace. How do you plan the play?

Review

You would have to be unlucky to go down in this contract, but you already have an indication that both club honours are lying badly. Can you succeed when the spade and diamond finesses are wrong as well?

Solution

If all the finesses are wrong you may yet find salvation in a 2–2 trump break – provided that you play your cards in the proper order. The diamond finesse must be taken first. Ruff a heart at trick three and play a low diamond for a finesse of the ten. If East produces the king he can do nothing to hurt you (assuming diamonds are not 5–1).

When the ten of diamonds wins at trick four, do not assume too readily that the finesse is working. Still, you can afford to try a trump finesse at this point. If West wins with the king and plays another club, go up with the ace, ruff the last heart, and cash a top spade. On a 3–1 trump break you will have to draw the last trump and fall back on a second diamond finesse. But if trumps are 2–2 it is bonus time. You can exit with the third club, not caring who has the king of diamonds.

The complete deal:

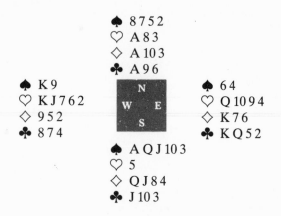

```
                    ♠ 8 7 5 2
                    ♡ A 8 3
                    ◇ A 10 3
                    ♣ A 9 6
  ♠ K 9                              ♠ 6 4
  ♡ K J 7 6 2          N             ♡ Q 10 9 4
  ◇ 9 5 2          W       E         ◇ K 7 6
  ♣ 8 7 4              S             ♣ K Q 5 2
                    ♠ A Q J 10 3
                    ♡ 5
                    ◇ Q J 8 4
                    ♣ J 10 3
```